It was <u>har</u>d <u>for</u> Hasan. There was a lot of w<u>ait</u>i<u>ng</u>.

"Can I have a t<u>ur</u>n?" said Hasan.
"No, you are <u>too</u> little. The wind
wi<u>ll</u> drag you a<u>long</u>," they said.

So Hasan st<u>oo</u>d in the p<u>ar</u>k, w<u>ai</u>t<u>ing</u> to get bigg<u>er</u>.

"Can I have a go?" said Hasan. "No, you are <u>too</u> little. It is <u>hard</u> to stand up and <u>harder</u> to stop!" they said.

So Hasan st<u>oo</u>d in the str<u>ee</u>t, w<u>ai</u>t<u>ing</u> to get bigg<u>er</u>.

"Can I join in?" said Hasan. "No, you are too little. You will hit it in the net," they said.

So Hasan st<u>oo</u>d n<u>ear</u> the net, w<u>ai</u>t<u>ing</u>
to get bigg<u>er</u>.

"Can I have just one go?" said Hasan.
"No, you are <u>too</u> little. You m<u>igh</u>t
land in the pond!" they said.

So Hasan st<u>oo</u>d n<u>ear</u> the pond,
w<u>ai</u>ti<u>ng</u> to get bigg<u>er</u>.

"Look! It's my turn now and you are too big!" said Hasan. That morning it was good to be the little one!

BIG BEN

AND THE
CLOCK TOWER

In 1834 the old Houses of Parliament were completely destroyed by fire, a spectacle witnessed by thousands of Londoners.

The following year a Commission was set up to organize a competition for the design of a new building. It was to be Gothic or Elizabethan in style, and from the 97 drawings submitted, the one selected included a clock tower.

This clock tower was destined to become one of the world's most recognized and best loved landmarks, while the measured tones of the huge bell at the top, known affectionately as Big Ben, have resolutely marked the passage of time and, for other nations around the globe, have been an audible reminder of the Mother of Parliaments and the spirit of freedom.

En 1834, l'ancien Palais du Parlement fut complètement détruit par un incendie, sous les yeux de milliers de Londoniens.

L'année suivante, on établit une Commission qui organiserait un concours pour un projet de nouveau Parlement. Le style devrait être gothique ou élisabéthain et, sur les 97 plans proposés, on choisit celui qui incorporait une tour d'horloge.

Cette tour allait devenir un point de repère connu et familier dans le monde entier, tandis que son carillon au rythme lent, affectueusement surnommé Big Ben, marquerait inlassablement le passage du temps et serait pour tous les pays un symbole sonore du Parlement et de l'esprit de liberté.

Im Jahre 1834 fiel das alte Parlamentsgebäude einem Brand zum Opfer, ein Drama, das sich vor den Augen Tausender von Londonern abspielte.

Im Jahr darauf wurde eine Kommission eingesetzt, die einen Wettbewerb für den Entwurf eines neuen Parlamentsgebäudes im gotischen oder elisabethanischen Stil ausschreiben sollte. Unter 97 Einsendungen wurde schließlich ein Entwurf mit Uhrturm ausgewählt.

Der Uhrturm sollte zu einem weltweit berühmten und beliebten Wahrzeichen der Stadt London werden. Der Schlag der riesigen Glocke oben im Turm, liebevoll Big Ben genannt, markiert zuverlässig den Ablauf der Zeit und hat zu Kriegszeiten die Nationen rund um die Welt an den Geist von Demokratie und Freiheit erinnert.

A Competition

🏴󠁧󠁢󠁥󠁮󠁧󠁿 The winning design was by Charles Barry, a well known architect of the day. The project was beset with administrative problems and it was several years before the new building and its clock tower were completed.

A second competition was held, limited to only a few contenders, to decide who should design and build the 'Great Clock of Westminster'. The high standards demanded led to much controversy, and eventually the clock was designed by an amateur, Edmund Beckett Denison. It was to be constructed by E. J. Dent, a highly respected clockmaker, but he died before the clock was finished and it was completed by his son in 1854.

▌▌ Le dessin gagnant fut celui de Charles Barry, architecte renommé à l'époque. Le projet se heurta à des problèmes d'administration et il fallut plusieurs années pour achever le bâtiment et sa tour. On organisa un second concours, entre quelques concurrents, pour décider du concepteur et bâtisseur de 'la Grande Horloge de Westminster'. Les critères imposés provoquèrent de nombreuses controverses et on choisit finalement un amateur, Edmund Beckett Denison. Le constructeur devait être E.J. Dent, horloger très réputé, mais il mourut avant d'avoir achevé l'horloge et ce fut son fils qui en termina la construction en 1854.

▬ Sieger des Wettbewerbs war Charles Barry, ein bekannter Architekt. Das Bauprojekt war mit verwaltungstechnischen Problemen belastet, und so dauerte es Jahre, bis das neue Gebäude und der Uhrturm fertiggestellt waren. Um einen passenden Entwurf für die 'Große Uhr von Westminster' zu finden, wurde ein zweiter Wettbewerb ausgeschrieben, zu dem nur wenige Teilnehmer zugelassen waren. Die hohen Anforderungen führten zu heftigen Auseinandersetzungen, und schließlich wurde der Entwurf eines Amateurs, Edmund Beckett Denison, angenommen. E.J. Dent, ein hochangesehener Uhrmacher, sollte die Uhr anfertigen. Da er jedoch starb, bevor die Uhr fertig war, führte sein Sohn diesen Auftrag im Jahre 1854 zu Ende.

The Clock Tower

🇬🇧 The different stone used in the construction of the tower was from Yorkshire, Cornwall and Caen (in France), and when it was complete the tower stood 314 feet (95.7m) tall. 334 steps lead up from the base to the belfry, with a further 59 steps up to the lantern at the very top. A light inside the lantern (known as the Ayrton Light) is lit whenever Parliament is at work after dark.

A third of the way up the tower is a Prison Room, last used in 1880; here a member of either the House of Commons or House of Lords could be detained for misbehaviour during a debate.

🇫🇷 La pierre différente utilisée pour la construction de la tour provenait du Yorkshire, de Cornouailles et de Caen. La tour achevée avait 95,7m de haut. 334 marches allaient de la base au beffroi, suivies de 59 marches pour accéder à la lanterne, tout en haut. Une lumière à l'intérieur de la lanterne ('the Ayrton Light') s'allume lorsque le Parlement siège de nuit.

A un tiers de la montée, dans la tour, se trouve une cellule de prison, utilisée pour la dernière fois en 1880, où on pouvait enfermer un membre de la Chambre des Communes ou des Lords s'il s'était mal conduit pendant un débat.

🇩🇪 Zum Bau des 95,7m hohen Turms wurden verschiedene Steinarten aus Yorkshire, Cornwall und Caen (in Frankreich) benutzt. 334 Stufen führen zum Glockenturm, und weitere 59 Stufen ganz hoch zur Laterne. Wenn das Parlament nach Einbruch der Dunkelheit tagt, wird in der Laterne das sogenannte Ayrton Licht angezündet.

In ein Drittelhöhe befindet sich ein Gefängnisraum, der zuletzt im Jahre 1880 benutzt wurde. Mitglieder des Unterhauses und des Oberhauses wurden darin in Verwahrung genommen, wenn sie sich bei Parlamentsdebatten ungebührlich aufführten.

95.7m

Big Ben

🇬🇧 The first great bell was cast in Stockton-on-Tees in 1856 and transported to London by train and sea. Because the tower was not complete, it was hung on gallows nearby and tested each day. In October 1857 a crack appeared, and the bell had to be broken up and recast, this time in Whitechapel in the East End of London. Just over a year later the new bell was slowly and carefully winched up a shaft inside the tower, and tolled over London for the first time in July 1859. But in the September it, too, cracked. The weight of the hammer was reduced, the bell was turned so that the hammer struck it on a different spot, and a small square was cut out of the bell to prevent the crack from spreading.

Big Ben is thought to have been named after Sir Benjamin Hall, the then Commissioner of Works, although it could also have been named after Benjamin Caunt, a famous prize fighter of the day. It is 9ft (2.7m) in diameter, $7^1/2$ft (2.2m) high and weighs $13^1/2$ tons (13,720kg).

🇫🇷 La première grosse cloche fut coulée à Stockton-on-Tees en 1856 et transportée jusqu'à Londres par voie ferroviaire et maritime. La tour n'était pas achevée, aussi on suspendit la cloche à une potence, à côté, et on l'essayait chaque jour. En octobre 1857, une félure se produisit et on dut casser la cloche et la refondre, à Whitechapel cette fois, dans l'East End de Londres. Un an plus tard environ, on hissait lentement la nouvelle cloche avec précaution à l'intérieur de la tour et elle sonna pour la première fois sur Londres en juillet 1859. Mais, en septembre, elle se félait à son tour. On réduisit le poids du marteau, on tourna la cloche de façon à ce que le marteau ne la frappe pas au même endroit et on découpa un petit carré pour empêcher que la félure ne s'étende.

Big Ben devrait son nom à Sir Benjamin Hall, Directeur des Travaux Publics, ou peut-être à Benjamin Caunt, célèbre boxeur de l'époque. La cloche a 2,7m de diamètre, 2,2m de hauteur et pèse près de 14 tonnes.

🇩🇪 Die erste große Glocke wurde im Jahre 1856 in Stockton-on-Tees gegossen und per Eisenbahn und Schiff nach London befördert. Weil der Turm noch nicht fertig war, wurde sie an einem Galgen aufgehängt und täglich probegeläutet. Im Oktober 1857 erschien ein Riß auf der Oberfläche, so daß die Glocke wieder eingeschmolzen und neu gegossen werden mußte, diesmal in Whitechapel, einem Stadtteil im Osten Londons. Knapp ein Jahr später wurde die Glocke langsam und vorsichtig durch einen Schacht im Turminneren hinaufgezogen. Im Juli 1859 ertönte sie erstmals über den Dächern von London. Als sie im darauffolgenden September ebenfalls Risse aufwies, verringerte man das Gewicht des Klöppels und drehte die Glocke so, daß er auf eine andere Stelle schlug. Um die Ausbreitung der Risse zu verhindern, schnitt man auch ein kleines, viereckiges Stück aus der Glocke.

Big Ben, wie die Glocke mit einem Durchmesser von 2,7m, einer Höhe von 2,2m und einem Gewicht von 13,72t heißt, soll nach Sir Benjamin Hall, dem damaligen Bauleiter, benannt sein. Ebenso gut könnte der Name aber auch auf Benjamin Caunt, einen damals berühmten Preisboxer, zurückgehen.

13,720kg

The Great Clock

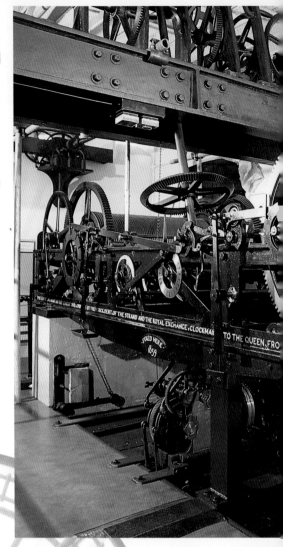

🇬🇧 The clock was made in London, and as it was completed before the tower was ready, it was kept in the factory and regularly tested. Several refinements and improvements were made as a result.

The balance of the clock is extremely fine. There is a small shelf on the pendulum rod on which sit a number of weights, including some old pennies. The addition of one penny causes the clock to gain two-fifths of a second in 24 hours. The clock is wound and checked for accuracy three times a week.

The Great Clock of Westminster began its life as London's official timekeeper on 31 May 1859.

🇫🇷 L'horloge, fabriquée à Londres, fut achevée avant la tour et resta à l'usine, où on la vérifiait périodiquement. Elle bénéficia ainsi de plusieurs perfectionnements et améliorations.

L'équilibre de l'horloge est extrêmement délicat. Le balancier est muni d'une petite tablette sur laquelle sont posés plusieurs poids, dont quelques anciens pennies. L'addition d'un penny fait avancer l'horloge de deux cinquièmes de seconde en 24 heures. L'horloge est remontée et vérifiée trois fois par semaine.

La Grande Horloge de Westminster est le chronomètre officiel de Londres depuis le 31 mai 1859.

🇩🇪 Die Uhr wurde in London hergestellt. Da sie vor dem Turm fertig war, wurde sie in der Fabrik aufbewahrt und regelmäßig getestet, mit dem Erfolg, daß sie technisch immer weiter verbessert wurde.

Die Unruh des Uhrwerks ist extrem empfindlich. An der Pendelstange befindet sich ein kleines Bord mit Gewichten und einigen alten Penny-Münzen. Kommt ein Penny hinzu, gewinnt die Uhr in 24 Stunden genau zwei Fünftelsekunden dazu. Dreimal wöchentlich wird die Uhr aufgezogen und daber auf Genauigkeit überprüft.

Die Große Uhr von Westminster, Londons offizieller Zeitmesser, ist seit dem 31. Mai 1859 in Betrieb.

1859

The Clock Faces

🇬🇧 Each of the four clock faces is 23ft (7m) in diameter and made up of 312 separate pieces of glass. The hour hands are 9ft (2.7m) long, made of gunmetal, and weigh about 6cwt (300kg) each. The minute hands are 14ft (4.2m) long, made of copper sheet, and weigh around 2cwt (100kg) each. Notice the Roman number IV has been used instead of the usual IIII preferred by horologists. Beneath each face, in Gothic lettering, there is an inscription in Latin – 'O Lord, make safe our Queen Victoria the First'.

Until 1906, when electricity was connected, the clock faces were illuminated at night by gaslight. Now each clock face is lit from behind by special energy-saving fluorescent bulbs.

🇫🇷 Chacun des quatre cadrans de l'horloge a 7m de diamètre et est composé de 312 morceaux de verre. Les petites aiguilles, en bronze à canon, ont 2,7m de long, et pèsent 300kg chacune environ. Les grandes aiguilles, en tôle de cuivre, ont 4,2m de long et pèsent environ 100kg chacune. Remarquez qu'on a utilisé le chiffre romain IV au lieu du IIII généralement préféré par les horlogers. En dessous de chaque cadran, en lettres gothiques, on peut lire une inscription latine: 'Seigneur, protégez notre Reine Victoria Ière'. Avant d'être branchés sur le secteur électrique, en 1906, les cadrans étaient éclairés la nuit au gaz. Actuellement, chaque cadran est illuminé par des ampoules fluorescentes qui économisent l'énergie.

🇩🇪 Jedes der vier Zifferblätter hat einen Durchmesser von 7m und besteht aus 312 einzelnen Glasscheiben. Die aus Rotguß gefertigten Stundenzeiger sind 2,7m lang und wiegen jeweils etwa 300kg. Die Minutenzeiger sind aus Kupferblech, 4,2m lang und wiegen jeweils etwa 100kg. Beachtenswert ist, daß statt der von Uhrmachern bevorzugten IIII eine römische IV verwendet wurde. Unterhalb jedes Zifferblattes befindet sich eine lateinische Inschrift in gotischen Lettern – 'Herr, schütze unsere Königin Viktoria I.'. Bis 1906, als der elektrische Betrieb aufgenommen wurde, wurden die Zifferblätter nachts durch Gaslaternen beleuchtet. Heutzutage erfolgt die Beleuchtung von hinten durch spezielle energiesparende Leuchtstofflampen.

7m

The Future

🇬🇧 In the 1980s decades of city grime were removed from the stonework and today the Clock Tower stands as clean and bright as the day it was built. The clock has suffered a few mishaps over the years, the worst occurring in 1976 when a metal shaft snapped and the clock mechanism was almost literally torn apart. Following extensive repairs, it was pronounced fit and well once more and ready for many more years of service.

With the invention of newer and more advanced clocks, can the Westminster Clock retain its place as – probably – the most widely known timekeeper in the world? Only Time itself will tell, but Big Ben and the Westminster Clock Tower will undoubtedly continue to be loved and cherished by many generations to come.

🇫🇷 Dans les années 1980, on a débarrassé la maçonnerie d'une accumulation de crasse urbaine et, aujourd'hui, la Tour de l'Horloge est aussi propre que lors de sa construction. L'horloge a subi quelques mésaventures, au cours des années, dont la pire en 1976, lorsqu'une tige métallique s'est cassée, arrachant presque les rouages du mouvement. Après d'importantes réparations, l'horloge a été déclarée en bon état de marche et prête à reprendre son service pendant de longues années encore.

Avec l'invention de nouvelles pendules plus perfectionnées, l'Horloge de Westminster pourra-t-elle conserver son rôle de chronomètre le plus célèbre (probablement) du monde? Seul le temps nous le dira, mais Big Ben et la Tour de l'Horloge de Westminster garderont certainement l'affection de nombreuses générations à venir.

🇩🇪 In den 80er Jahren wurden die Steinfassaden von jahrzehntealten Schmutzbelägen befreit, und heute ist der Uhrturm so sauber und glänzend wie zur Zeit seiner Erbauung. Die Uhr kam im Laufe der Zeit einige Male zu Schaden. Am schlimmsten war es, als 1976 ein Metallschaft zerbrach und das Uhrwerk buchstäblich fast zerrissen wurde. Nach umfassender Reparatur war die Funktion der Uhr aber wieder auf Jahre hinaus gesichert.

Da es mittlerweile neuere und bessere Uhren gibt, stellt sich die Frage, ob die Uhr von Westminster, der wahrscheinlich bekannteste Zeitmesser der Welt, ihren Platz auch weiter behalten kann. Aber zweifelsohne werden auch zukünftige Generationen Big Ben und den Uhrturm von Westminster lieben und schätzen.

Many months to repair se

BIG BEN I. OUT FOR THE COUN

BIG BEN stopped with a rattle and a bang at 3.45 a.m. today . . . and it will be out of action for many months. It happened when a cast iron frame holding the mechanism cracked, hurling huge pieces of metal about

I'm not a

EVENING NEWS REPORTER

hour bells was thrown on to the floor.

"We are still examining the damage but it will take months to fix," said Mr. Leslie Butler, the man in charge of

Commons.

Police on duty at t Commons reported - stran noises coming from t clock tower.

Then the "quarter to chime bell rang twice, in stead of once.

Mr. Butler, aged 64, live